ANCIENT
ROMANS
Sticker Book

Licensed exclusively to Top That Publishing Ltd
Tide Mill Way, Woodbridge, Suffolk, IP12 IAP, UK
www.topthatpublishing.com
Copyright © 2015 Tide Mill Media
All rights reserved
246897531
Printed and bound in China

Rome is where the heart is!

Welcome to Rome, the centre of one of the richest and most powerful empires ever seen! Streets were noisy with people talking, children playing and the sound of chariots and hooves on the stone paving. Can you spot the public baths and the outdoor lesson?

Ancient Rome was covered in graffiti. 'Lucius pinxit' means 'Lucius painted this'.

This shop sells olive oil. Oil was important for cooking, cleaning, and as fuel for lamps.

Create your own Roman street sticker scene!

Don't forget your stylus

Education was important to Romans, but you only went to lessons if your parents could afford it. Most children didn't go to school because their parents needed them to work. Reading, writing and basic maths were taught, but books weren't used – they were much too expensive!

Complete the empire by adding red stickers over the gaps!

The bath house

People went to public baths to wash and to meet friends. There were three rooms – a warm room, a hot room and a cold room. After the warm room, you moved to the hot room, where perfumed oil was rubbed onto you and then scraped off again. After that, it was into the cold bath. Brrrr!

Under attack!

The strength of the Roman army was legendary! Soldiers were paid, well organised and had standard equipment – unlike most of their enemies. In battle, a Roman soldier or 'legionary' first threw his spear, then fought with his sword. Soldiers also carried a wooden shield and wore metal armour and a helmet. This fort is under attack!

War machines

The Roman army used deadly 'siege engines' to attack walled strongholds. Massive crossbows called 'ballistas' fired heavy iron arrows, and catapults launched large stones against the enemy's walls. The heavy beam of a battering ram had an iron end, shaped like a ram's head, that could smash through an enemy's walls. Here it comes!

A VERY big tortoise!

The 'testudo' – Latin for tortoise – was an impressive example of Roman discipline and organization. Soldiers bunched into a tight formation and used their shields to protect themselves against enemy fire – arrows just glanced off their curved shields! In this way, Roman soldiers could get close to their enemy without getting hurt.

Rome wasn't built in a day

The engineering achievements of Ancient Rome weren't matched until the 19th and 20th centuries! Their roads, aqueducts and buildings amazed the 'barbarians' they conquered. Roads and aqueducts were built so well that they survived for thousands of years ... you can still see some today!

The army was in charge of building roads, but slaves did lots of the work. About 10-15 per cent of the empire's population were slaves, rising to 35-40 per cent in Italy.

Create your own Construction sticker scene!

Aqueducts

Aqueducts were man-made waterways that carried water from the countryside to cities like Rome. Where aqueducts crossed a valley they looked a bit like a bridge, but a lot of aqueducts were tunnels or at ground level. In the city, the water supplied public baths, toilets and the street basins where most people got their water from.

All roads lead to Rome!

Roads connected the empire and allowed quick and efficient transport of goods, citizens and soldiers! Roads were made of earth, sand, gravel, cement and crushed rubble (up to 1.2 metres deep) with large, smooth stones on top.

Roman banquet

Ordinary Romans mostly ate bread and porridge, but the rich really knew how to throw a dinner party. Guests lay on couches, propping themselves on their left arm and eating with their right. These sorts of dinner parties were just for special occasions.

Create your own Banquet sticker scene!

Do you want fish sauce with that dormouse?

There were lots of strange foods at a banquet, and Romans certainly liked olives - there were at least 30 varieties! Most important was a fish sauce made from the fermented intestines of small fish. It was used as seasoning, as a condiment like salt, or as a sauce.

Children's games

Children were rarely invited to banquets. If they were, they would have been very well-behaved. If children talked back to their parents, the head of the household could throw them out of the house and never allow them back! But children still had fun ... you might even recognize some of their toys and games.

Gladiators, are you ready?

Armed combatants, called gladiators, entertained people in violent battles with other gladiators and animals. Large amphitheatres, like the Colosseum in Rome, were built especially to stage the fighting contests. Fighters were treated like heroes ... if they survived!

Stick an excited spectator here!

All kinds of wild animals featured – tigers, bulls, wolves, cheetahs, hippos, rhinos ...

Gladiator games were usually paired with beast contests. This one is getting a bit out of hand!

Colosseum 80,000 capacity

Gladiator games were big business and there were over 30 different types of gladiator.

To be sure a losing gladiator was dead, attendants whacked him with a hammer.

Fighting outfits

Fights normally took place between gladiators of different types, who each had different armour and weapons. These two gladiators have equipment designed to match each other and to make it a close fight!

Stick the murmillo's helmet here!

If slave gladiators fought well, they were sometimes given a wooden sword and their freedom.

I'd rather be catching fish!

Stick the arm guard here!

Stick a big heavy shield here!

Trident

Stick padded leg armour here!

Retarius
Light and agile, the retarius' best chance was to tire his opponent and trap him with his net.

Murmillo
Short and strong, the murmillo carried a heavy sword and shield, and had a padded left leg. He swung and stabbed at close quarters.

Dress the murmillo, ready for battle!

Training school

Gladiators were usually slaves or criminals, but some people chose to become one! If they fought well they could win prizes or gifts – they could also become famous. Gladiators lived in a training school, where they worked hard practising their skills. Gladiators were expensive to train, and were fed well. They only fought a few times a year.

Circus Maximus

Chariot racing was even more popular than gladiator fighting, and the Circus Maximus in Rome was the place to see it! Chariot racing was exciting and dangerous. Charioteers were allowed to bang into each other, so there were frequently terrible crashes ... look out!

Create your own Circus Maximus sticker scene!

Cheek to cheek

Public toilets were really very 'public'! Up to 30 people sat next to each other on a long bench – with no dividing walls for privacy! The public toilet was a good place to catch up with the latest gossip, or talk about politics. Don't be shy!

LUCIUS PINXIT

The bath house

Under attack!

War machines

A VERY big tortoise

Construction sticker scene

Fighting outfits

Training school

Aqueducts

Gladiators, are you ready?